NUMBER TRACING

for preschoolers

AGES **3+**

YOUR PHOTO

This book belongs to:

• COLOR IT

+WEEKLY BONUS

ARGOPREP

At ArgoPrep we believe in creating smart learning solutions
so that every student can succeed in life.

We would love to hear your honest feedback and review of our workbooks on Amazon.

Want weekly BONUS & FREE Tracing worksheets?

Visit our website at **www.argoprep.com/tracing** to download and print more

awesome tracing worksheets for your child.

Aknowlegments:
Icons made by Freepik, Smashicons, Turkkub, Vectors Market, Dmotry Mirolubov, Baianat, Roundicons, Zlatko Najdenovski, Pixel Perfect, Twitter, DinosoftLabs, Prettycons
from www.flaticon.com

Practice writing your name!

Instructions on how to use this workbook!

① ② ③ Follow the tracing pattern in order to easily trace the number!

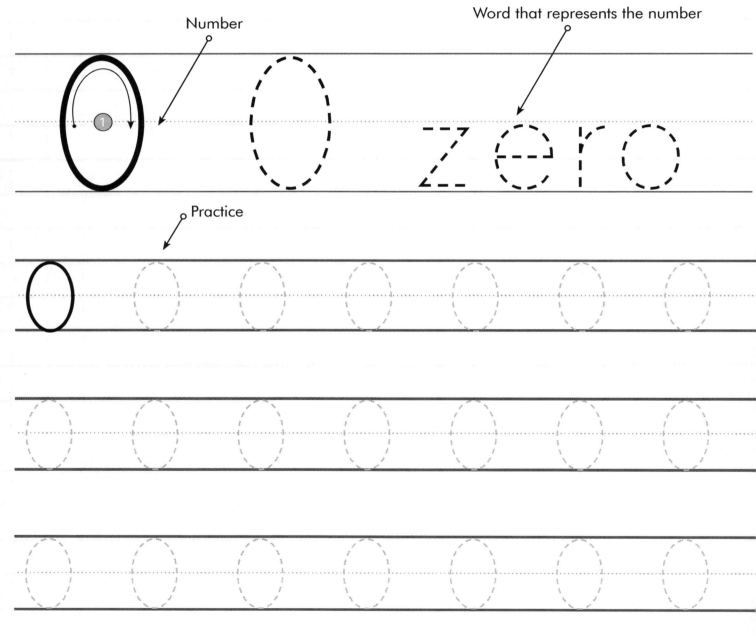

Number

Word that represents the number

zero

Practice

0 1 2 3 4 5 6 7 8 9 10 11 12 13 14 15 16 17 18 19 20

ARGOPREP

Zero Zero Zero Zero Zero Zero Zero

Practice writing the words!

LET'S BEGIN OUR
LETTER TRACING
JOURNEY

ZERO

0

O zero

0

ARGOPREP

Zero Zero Zero Zero Zero Zero Zero

ONE

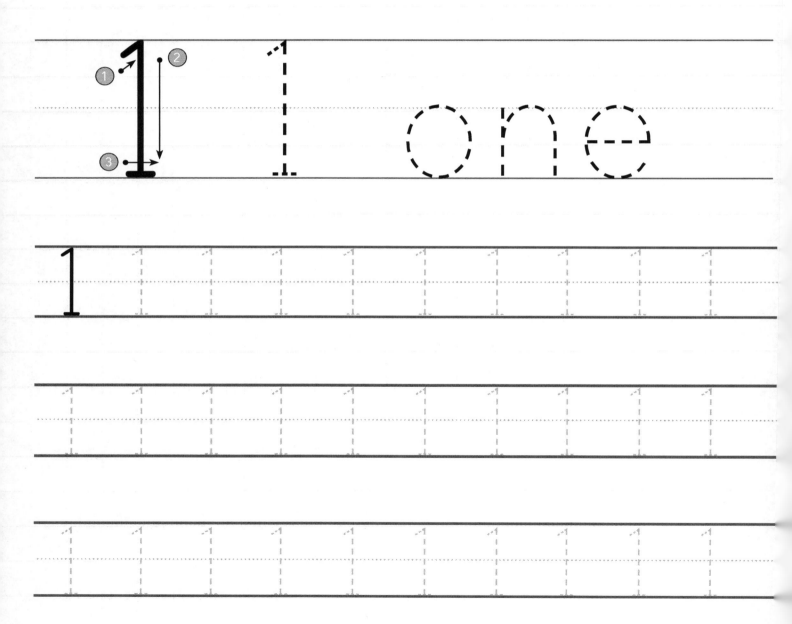

1 one

ARGOPREP

One One One One One One One One

TWO 2

2   2   two

2

0 1 **2** 3 4 5 6 7 8 9 10 11 12 13 14 15 16 17 18 19 20

Two Two Two Two Two Two Two

2 2 2 2 2 2 2

2 2 2 2 2 2 2

2 2 2 2 2 2 2

2 2 2 2 2 2 2

2 2 2 2 2 2 2

2 2 2 2 2 2

THREE

3   3   three

3   3   3   3   3   3   3

3   3   3   3   3   3   3

3   3   3   3   3   3   3

ARGOPREP

Three Three Three Three Three

3 3 3 3 3 3 3

3 3 3 3 3 3 3

3 3 3 3 3 3 3

3 3 3 3 3 3 3

3 3 3 3 3 3 3

3 3 3 3 3 3 3

FOUR

ARGOPREP

Four Four Four Four Four Four Four

FIVE

Five Five Five Five Five Five Five Five

5 5 5 5 5 5 5 5 5 5 5

5 5 5 5 5 5 5 5 5 5

5 5 5 5 5 5 5 5 5 5

5 5 5 5 5 5 5 5 5

5 5 5 5 5 5 5 5 5

5 5 5 5 5 5 5 5 5 5

ARGOPREP

SIX

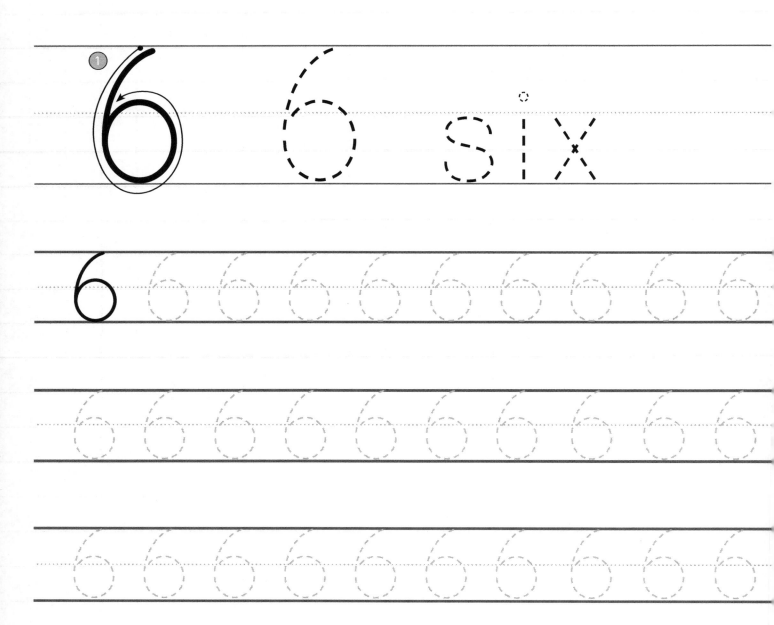

6 6 six

6

SEVEN

7 7 seven

7

Seven Seven Seven Seven Seven

EIGHT

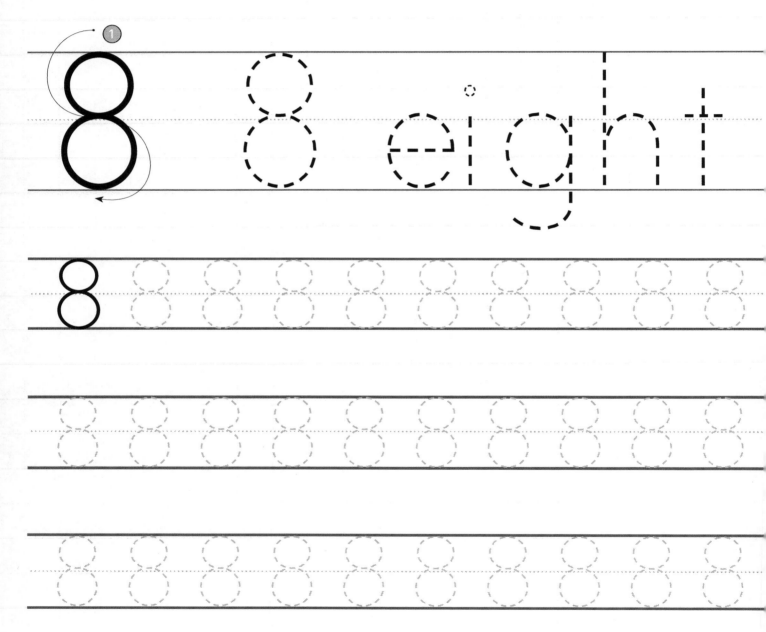

Eight Eight Eight Eight Eight Eight

8 8 8 8 8 8 8 8 8 8

8 8 8 8 8 8 8 8 8 8

8 8 8 8 8 8 8 8 8 8

8 8 8 8 8 8 8 8 8 8

8 8 8 8 8 8 8 8 8 8

8 8 8 8 8 8 8 8 8 8

ARGOPREP

NINE

9 9 nine

9 9 9 9 9 9 9 9 9 9

9 9 9 9 9 9 9 9 9

9 9 9 9 9 9 9 9 9

ARGOPREP

Nine Nine Nine Nine Nine Nine Nine

9 9 9 9 9 9 9 9 9 9

9 9 9 9 9 9 9 9 9 9

9 9 9 9 9 9 9 9 9 9

9 9 9 9 9 9 9 9 9 9

9 9 9 9 9 9 9 9 9 9

9 9 9 9 9 9 9 9 9 9

ARGOPREP

TEN

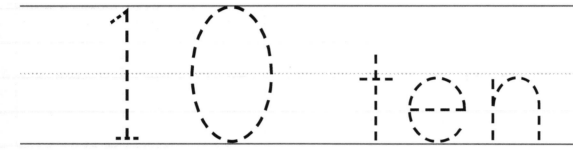

10

Ten Ten Ten Ten Ten Ten Ten Ten Ten

ELEVEN

11   eleven

11

ARGOPREP

Eleven Eleven Eleven Eleven Eleven

1 1 1 1 1 1 1 1 1 1 1

1 1 1 1 1 1 1 1 1 1

1 1 1 1 1 1 1 1 1 1

1 1 1 1 1 1 1 1 1 1 1

1 1 1 1 1 1 1 1 1 1 1

1 1 1 1 1 1 1 1 1 1 1

TWELVE

12   twelve

12 12 12 12 12 12

12 12 12 12 12 12

12 12 12 12 12 12

ARGOPREP

Twelve Twelve Twelve Twelve Twelve

12 12 12 12 12

12 12 12 12 12

12 12 12 12 12

12 12 12 12 12

12 12 12 12 12

12 12 12 12 12

ARGOPREP

THIRTEEN

13 thirteen

13 13 13 13 13

13 13 13 13 13

13 13 13 13 13

Thirteen Thirteen Thirteen Thirteen

13   13   13   13   13

13   13   13   13   13

13   13   13   13   13

13   13   13   13   13

13   13   13   13   13

13   13   13   13   13

FOURTEEN

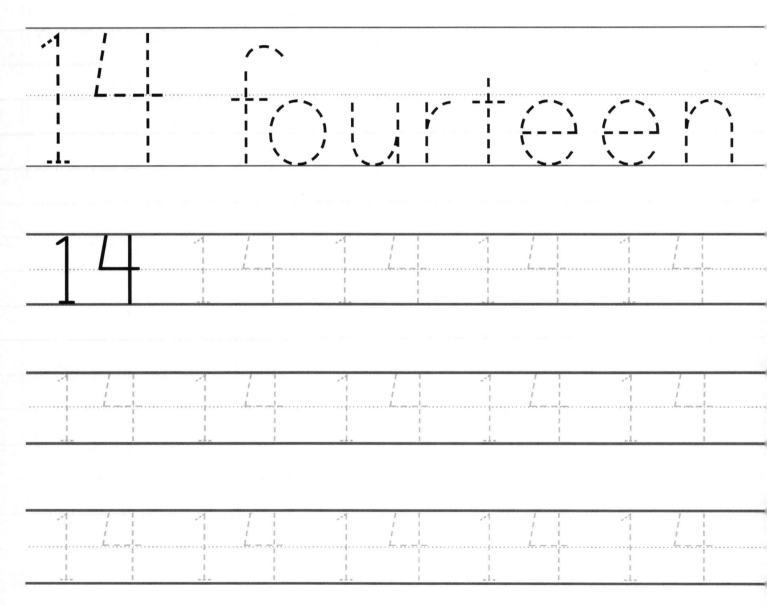

14 fourteen

14

ARGOPREP

Fourteen Fourteen Fourteen Fourteen

FIFTEEN

15 fifrteen

15

ARGOPREP

Fifteen Fifteen Fifteen Fifteen

15 15 15 15 15

15 15 15 15 15

15 15 15 15 15

15 15 15 15 15

15 15 15 15 15

15 15 15 15 15

SIXTEEN

16

sixteen

16

Sixteen Sixteen Sixteen Sixteen

16 16 16 16 16

16 16 16 16 16

16 16 16 16 16

16 16 16 16 16

16 16 16 16 16

16 16 16 16 16

ARGOPREP

SEVENTEEN

17 seventeen

17 17 17 17 17 17

17 17 17 17 17

17 17 17 17 17

Seventeen Seventeen Seventeen

EIGHTEEN

18 eighteen

18

Eighteen Eighteen Eighteen Eighteen

18 18 18 18 18

18 18 18 18 18

18 18 18 18 18

18 18 18 18 18

18 18 18 18 18

18 18 18 18 18

ARGOPREP

NINETEEN

19 nineteen

19 19 19 19 19 19

19 19 19 19 19

19 19 19 19 19

Nineteen Nineteen Nineteen Nineteen

19 19 19 19 19

19 19 19 19 19

19 19 19 19 19

19 19 19 19 19

19 19 19 19 19

19 19 19 19 19

TWENTY

20   twenty

20   20   20   20   20

20   20   20   20   20

20   20   20   20   20

ARGOPREP

20 20 20 20 20 20

20 20 20 20 20 20

20 20 20 20 20 20

20 20 20 20 20 20

20 20 20 20 20 20

20 20 20 20 20 20

ARGOPREP

PRACTICE
NUMBER
TRACING &
COUNTING

How many apples
do you see?

Trace your answer below.

How many boys do you see?

Trace your answer below.

How many cars do you see?

Trace your answer below.

ARGOPREP

How many animals do you see?

Trace your answer below.

Can you write the names of the animals you recognize?

How many flowers do you see?

Trace your answer below.

ARGOPREP

How many same flags do you see?

Trace your answer below.

How many chicks does the chicken have?

Trace your answer below.

Name all of the chicks!

How many windows do you see?

Trace your answer below.

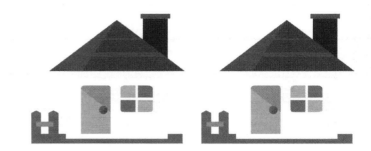

How many ice cream cones are there?

Trace your answer below.

How many ocean creatures do you see?

Trace your answer below.
Name all these creatures!

How many figers do you have on your hands?

Trace your answer below.

How many vegetables are among the fruits?

Trace your answer below.

How many same butterflies do you see?

Trace your answer below.

How many small mushrooms are there?

Trace your answer below.

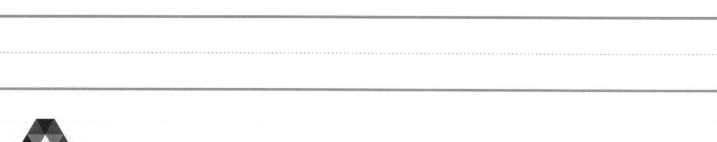

How many circles are inside the triangle?

Trace your answer below.

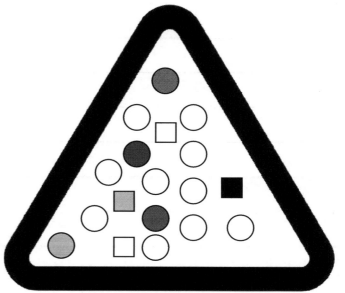

How many stars can you fit in the shape shown?

Trace your answer below.

★	★					

How many insects do you see?
Can you name any?

Trace your answer below.

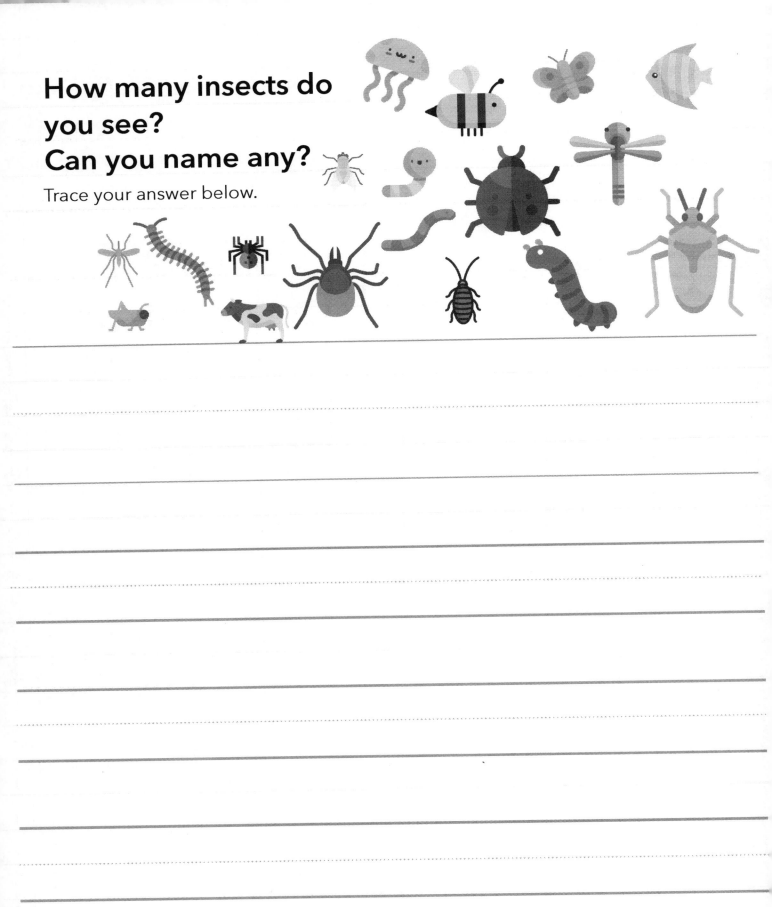

If you turn the number 9 upside down, what number do you see?

Trace your answer below.

How many stars are in the sky?

Trace your answer below.

ARGOPREP

Count how many flags are on the mountain.

Trace your answer below.

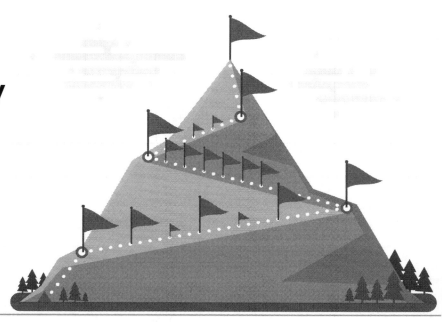

How many people in total do you see?

Trace your answer below.

BONUS!
COLOR IT

Apple   Mango   Orange

Strawbery   Cherry   Grape

Broccoli   Onion   Carrot

Eggplant   Cucumber   Asparagus

ARGOPREP

Dog, Cat, Pig

Panda

Made in the USA
San Bernardino, CA
25 June 2018